This is Princess Aurora.

She walks in the forest today.

Princess Aurora likes birds and animals.

They live in the forest.

Prince Phillip likes the Princess and she likes him.

Princess Aurora lives in a big castle.

Oh, no! Maleficent is in the castle.
She is bad.

Princess Aurora sees a spindle.
She puts one hand on the spindle.

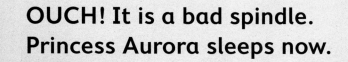

OUCH! It is a bad spindle.
Princess Aurora sleeps now.

She sleeps and sleeps and sleeps.

Prince Phillip is on a horse.

He goes in the castle.

Prince Phillip kisses Princess Aurora.
She looks at the Prince.

Now the Prince and Princess are happy.

Activities

Before You Read

1 **Say Yes/No.**

1 The birds live in the forest.
2 They like the girl.
3 She is beautiful.
4 She has a yellow dress.
5 The girl likes the birds.

After You Read

1 **Put the pictures in the right order.**

☐ ☐ ☐ ☐ ☐ ☐

2 **Match the sentences and pictures.**

1 He likes the Princess.
2 She is bad.
3 She sleeps and sleeps.
4 They are happy.

Pearson Education Limited
Edinburgh Gate, Harlow,
Essex CM20 2JE, England
and Associated Companies throughout the world.

ISBN: 978-1-4082-8851-1

This edition first published by Pearson Education Ltd 2012

1 3 5 7 9 10 8 6 4 2

Set in 19/23pt OT Fiendstar Semibold
Printed in China
SWTC/01

Published by Pearson Education Ltd in association with
Penguin Books Ltd, both companies being subsidiaries of Pearson Plc

For a complete list of the titles available in the Penguin Kids series please go to www.penguinreaders.com.
Alternatively, write to your local Pearson Longman office or to: Penguin Readers Marketing Department,
Pearson Education, Edinburgh Gate, Harlow, Essex CM20 2JE, England.